7/94
BOOKS
2.98

MW00615578

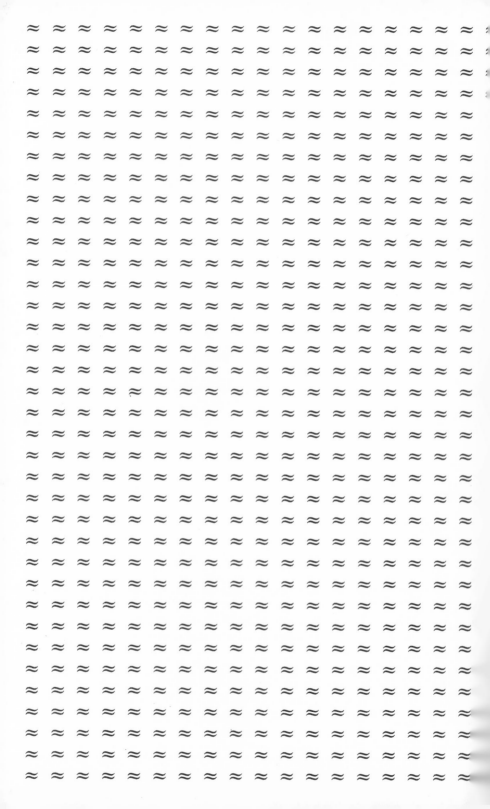

TRUSTING YOUR LIFE TO WATER AND ETERNITY

Trusting Your Life
To Water and Eternity

TWENTY POEMS
OF
OLAV H. HAUGE

❧

Chosen and Translated
by
Robert Bly

❧

Graphics by
Kaare Espolin Johnson

❧

MILKWEED EDITIONS

© 1987 by Robert Bly
All rights reserved. Published 1987
Printed in the United States of America

89 88 87   5 4 3 2 1

Published by *Milkweed Editions*
Post Office Box 3226
Minneapolis, Minnesota 55403
Books may be ordered from the above address

ISBN: 0-915943-28-X
Library of Congress Catalog Card Number: 87-42897

This publication is supported in part by grants provided by The Norwegian Cultural Council; the Arts Development Fund of United Arts; the Dayton Hudson Foundation for Daytons and Target stores; The First Bank Systems; the Jerome Foundation; the Metropolitan Regional Arts Council with Special Assistance from the McKnight Foundation; and by the contributions of generous individuals.

Preface

Olav H. Hauge announces right away what he wants: "Don't come to me with the entire truth." Olav H. Hauge asks that we bring only a "hint" when he asks for truth, and as a model for such discretion, mentions that birds carry away from a lake only a few drops of water, and the wind takes from the ocean a single grain of salt.

He adopts his own advice in poetry, and brings to the reader in each poem a single grain of wheat. He writes from inside the economy of scarcity. As Lewis Hyde mentions in his book *The Gift*, the gift-giving society has some association with the economy of scarcity. When commercial society arrives, things are bought and sold; but nothing in these poems seems saleable, and they are intended as gifts.

Norway's culture from ancient times has been a culture of scarcity. During the Middle Ages a man or woman's only private possessions might be a wooden spoon and a bowl, and in some houses there were no bowls, so that the food was set directly on the wooden table, and the hollows worn away by the spoons show still. Olav H. Hauge was born and still lives in Ulvik, a village in the Hardanger Fjord area, where apple farming was developed in the nineteenth century. He has lived his whole life on the proceeds from a single acre of apples, which he has cared for alone. The richness in his small house lies in the hand-made objects and in the bookcases, from which ancient Chinese poets encourage him in the "grain of salt" theory. The best poetry from many continents finds its way to this house that is only apparently isolated.

Robert Francis in the United States shared his way of living, and Francis' poems resemble Hauge's, which are more like hummingbirds than geese, more like mink tracks in the snow than the mink itself. Hauge belongs to Eberhart's, Tate's and Rexroth's generation. He was born in 1908, and is now in good health, and still farming apples. He married for the first time five years ago, to Bodil Cappelen, the artist.

It is an honor to introduce his work in the United States, and I'm grateful to Milkweed Editions for publishing the book, and for agreeing to include some of the woodcuts by Kaare Espolin Johnson. Johnson is a Norwegian artist roughly Hauge's age, who lives now in Oslo. Both men work often in black and white, and neither tries to cheer the reader up with bright colors. Olav H. Hauge offers us scarcity and suffering. He knows what it is like to ride down the mountain as dusk falls, merely going farther and farther down, or what it's like to climb a mountain steeply, arrive at the hut, and find nothing there except a black cooking kettle overturned with its prong-feet pointed toward you. He doesn't say that swamps are easy to cross, or that we should trust them, but reminds us of those who have drowned: "he, really crazy, trusted his life to water and eternity."

Robert Bly

Contents

Kom Ikkje Med
Heile Sanningi

Kom ikkje med heile sanningi,
kom ikkje med havet for min torste.
kom ikkje med himmelen når eg bed um ljos,
men kom med ein glimt, ei dogg, eit fjom,
som fuglane ber med seg vassdropar frå lauget
og vinden eit korn av salt.

Don't Come To Me
With The Entire Truth

Don't come to me with the entire truth.
Don't bring the ocean if I feel thirsty,
nor heaven if I ask for light;
but bring a hint, some dew, a particle,
as birds carry only drops away from water,
and the wind a grain of salt.

Eg Dreg Ifrå Glaset

Eg dreg ifrå glaset fyrr eg legg meg,
eg vil sjå det levande myrkret når eg vaknar,
og skogen og himmelen. Eg veit ei grav
som ikkje har glugg mot stjernone.
No er Orion komen i vest, alltid jagande —
han er ikkje komen lenger enn eg.
Kirsebærtreet utanfor er nake og svart.
I den svimlande blå himmelklokka
ritar morgonmånen med hard nagl.

I Open The Curtain

Before I go to bed I open the curtains.
When I wake up I want to see the living dark
and the pines and sky. I know a grave;
if you're there you do not see the stars.

Orion has arrived now in the west, hunting, hunting –
he has not come any farther than I have.
The cherry tree outside my window is naked and black.
The sky is a bell, dizzingly blue, where the hard
fingernail of the new moon is writing something.

Det Ryk

Lett og glad stig røyken
frå pipa i skogen,
der dei tvo unge bur.
Dei ofrar til ljosmaktene
med gladt hjarta
feit fure,
har bjørk.

I knipargard er røyken
spinken og tunn:
Skrale tider,
lite vert det
til Gud.

Du ser ikkje
din eigen røyk.
Men eg sat ofte
mryk
som Kain.

Smoke

The smoke floats up lightly from the chimney
in the trees, where
the young couple lives.
In joy they give to
the great light-powers
thick spruce,
and hard birch.

Where the miser lives the smoke
is spinkly and thin:
Evil times,
not much available
for God.

You never see
your own smoke.
But for years I sat
like Cain
in the dark.

Kuppern Skrid I Squaw Valley

Eg har òg teke premi på skeisor, eg vart
nummer fire i eit skulerenn då eg var åtte,
etter han Leiv.
Men dei hine hadde stålsette skeisor,
og eg berre jarn.
Eg hadde kjøpt mine hjå urmakaren,
eg tok dei som hadde
største snablane.

Men no skrid Kuppern i Squaw Valley!
Eg har ikkje tenkt å gå nokon 10 000 m,
men ordi fær ein djervare sving,
og ho mor grip fastare um staven.

Kuppern On Skates In Squaw Valley

I also won a prize on skates, I was
number four in a schoolrace
when I was eight, after Leiv, he won.
But they had steel skates,
and I had only iron.
I had bought mine at a watchmaker's,
and I took those
with the biggest curlecues.

And now in Squaw Valley Kuppern is winning on skates!
I hadn't planned on the 10,000 meter,
but the words take on a wilder tone
and my mother takes
a fiercer grip on her walking stick.

Vintermorgon

Då eg vakna i dag, var rutone tilfrosne,
men eg glødde av ein god draum.
Og omnen slo varme ut i romet
frå ein kubbe han hadde godna seg med um natti.

Winter Morning

When I woke this morning the panes were frosted over,
but I glowed from a good dream.
And the stove poured out its warmth
from a woodblock it had enjoyed the whole night.

Bertolt Brecht

Bertolt Brecht var ein mangslungen kar.
Dramatikar, skodespelar, diktar.
Verseformi hans var tiltrøyvi,
ho stod på dørhella
som eit par tresko.

Berthold Brecht

Berthold Brecht was a complicated man.
Playwright, actor, poet.
His verse forms were easy to get hold of.
They stood on the stoop
like a pair of wooden shoes.

I Dag Kjende Eg

I dag kjende eg
at eg hadde laga eit godt dikt.
Fuglane kvitra i hagen då eg kom ut,
og soli stod blid yver Bergahaugane.

Today I Understood

Today I understood
that I had made a good poem.
The birds called in the orchard as I came out,
and the sun stood there mild over the Bergafjell.

Yver Hengjemyri

Det er rotstokkane av alle trei som har stupt
ut i her, som gjer du kan gå
trygt yver myri.
Slike stokkar held seg lenge, dei kan
ha lege her i hundratals år,
og endå er det eit morke skrimsel
att av dei under mosen,
dei er enno med og ber
so du kjem frelst yver.
Og når du skyv ut på fjellvatnet,
kjenner du at minnet um den kaldingen
som drukna seg her ein gong,
er med og ber den skrale pråmen.
Han, den galningen, trudde livet sitt
til vatnet og æva.

Across The Swamp

It is the roots from all the trees that have died
out here, that's how you can walk
safely over the soft places.
Roots like these keep their firmness, it's possible
they've lain here centuries.
And there is still some dark remains
of them under the moss.
They are still in the world and hold
you up so you can make it over.
And when you push out into the mountain lake, high
up, you feel how the memory
of that cold person
who drowned himself here once
helps hold up your frail boat.
He, really crazy, trusted his life
to water and eternity.

Det Er Ikkje So Fårleg

Det er ikkje so fårleg
um grashoppa skjerper ljåen.
Men når tussalusi kviskrar,
skal du akta deg.

There Is Nothing So Scary

There is nothing so scary
about grasshoppers sharpening scythes.
But when the troll's flea whispers,
be careful.

Eg Stend Eg, Seddu

Eg stend eg, seddu.
Eg stod her i fjor òg eg, seddu.
Eg kjem til å stå her eg, seddu.
Eg tek det eg, seddu.
Du veit ikkje noko du, seddu.
Du er nyss komen du, seddu.
Kor lenge skal me stå her?
Me fær vel eta, seddu.
Eg stend når eg et òg eg, seddu.
Og kastar fatet i veggen.
Me fær vel kvila, seddu.
Me fær vel sova, seddu.
Me fær vel pissa og skita òg, seddu.
Kor lenge skal me stå her?
Eg stend eg, seddu.
Eg tek det eg, seddu.
Eg kjem til å stå her, eg, seddu.

I Stand Here, Do You Understand

I stand here, do you understand.
I stood here last year too, do you understand.
I am going to stand here too, do you understand.
I take it too, do you understand.
There's something you don't know, do you understand.
You just got here, do you understand.
How long are we to stand here?
We have to eat too, do you understand.
I stand when I eat too, I do that, do you understand,
and throw the plates at the wall.
We have to rest too, do you understand.
We have to piss and shit too, do you understand.
How long are we to stand here?
I stand all right, do you understand.
I take it too, do you understand.
I'm going to stand here, do you understand.

På Høgdi

Etter lang vandring på uframkomelege vegar
er du uppe på høgdi.
Motgangen kuva deg ikkje, du trødde han
under deg, steig høgare.

Slik ser du det. Etter at livet har slengt deg
i frå seg og du slumpa til å hamna ovanpå,
lik ein einføtt trehest på sorpdungen.
Livet er miskunnsamt, det blindar og synkverver
og lagnaden akslar vår bør:
Dårskap og ovmod vert berg og blautmyrar,
hat og agg vert sår etter piler frå ovundsmenn,
og tvilen som grev oss, vert
kalde utturka gjel.

Du gjeng inn i bui.
På gruvesteinen ligg gryta kvelvd
og sprikjer fiendsleg med svarte føter.

Up On Top

After stumbling a long time over impossible trails
you are up on top.
Hardship didn't crush you, you trod it
down, climbed higher.

That's how *you* see it. After life has tossed you
away, and you ended up on top
like a one-legged wooden horse on a dump.
Life is merciful, it blinds and provides illusions,
and destiny takes on our burden:
foolishness and arrogance become mountains and marshy places,
hate and resentment become wounds from enemy arrows,
and the doubt always with us becomes cold dry
rock valleys.

You go in the door.
The pot lies upside down on the hearth,
it sprawls with hostile black feet.

Eit Ord

Eit ord
—ein stein
i ei kald elv.
Ein stein til—
Eg må ha mange steinar
skal eg koma over.

One Word

One word
—one stone
in a cold river.
One more stone—
I'll need many stones
if I'm going to get over.

Midvinter. Snø

Midvinter. Snø.
Eg gjev fuglane ei brødskorpe.
Og søv ikkje ringare for det.

Midwinter. Snow.

Midwinter. Snow.
I gave the birds a piece of bread.
And it didn't affect my sleep.

Desembermånen 1969

Han løyner stålet
i ei slire av sylv.
Det er blod på eggi.

December Moon 1969

It hides its steel
in a silver sheath.
On the edge there is blood.

Enno Rid Du Ved Sida

Enno rid du
ved sida
med soleld
i fakset,
gneistar og hovslag
kling
i dølne fjell—
enno rid du
vid sida
i regnet
og vinden
som tetnar
kring stigen
som hallar—
ned ber det, til botns ber det,
eg veit ikkje meir, og haustmyrkret fell.

You Ride On Still

You ride on still
at my side,
the setting sun
in the mane,
sparks and hoofsounds
ring out
through the secluded mountain—
you ride on still
at my side,
through rain falling
in the wind
that stiffens
on this trail
that slants down
steeper and steeper—
it goes down, it keeps going straight to the bottom,
this is all I know, and the autumn night comes down.

Eg Ser På Stempelen
På Fyrste Brevet Ditt

Eg ser på stempelen på fyrste brevet ditt.
Det er alt ein månad sidan det kom.
Den tidi har du heimsøkt huset,
lokka meg, søkt meg, skift
frå Ate til grøn erinnye.
I dag fekk eg biletet ditt:
Ei bleik gjente sit åleine på nokre stokkar
attmed eit skymrande vatn.

I Look At The Stamp

I look at the stamp on your first letter.
It's a month or more since it came.
During that time you've haunted this house,
called to me, frightened me, changed
from Ate to a green Erinye.
Today I got your photograph:
it is a girl sitting alone on some logs
near the darkening ocean.

Du Var Vinden

Eg er ein båt
utan vind.
Du var vinden.
Var det den leidi eg skulde?
Kven spør etter leidi
når ein har slik vind!

You Are The Wind

I am a boat
without wind.
You were the wind.
Was that the direction I wanted to go?
Who cares about directions
with a wind like that!

Eg Ser
På Ein Gamal Spegel

Framsida spegel.
Baksida eit bilete av Edens hage.

Eit underleg påfunn
av den gamle glasmeisteren.

Looking At An Old Mirror

The front a mirror.
The back a picture of the Garden of Eden.

A strange find
of the old master of glass.

Lauvhyttor Og Snøhus

Det er ikkje mykje med
desse versi, berre
nokre ord røysa saman
på slump.
Eg synest
likevel
det er gildt
å laga dei, då
har eg som eit hus
ei liti stund.
Eg kjem i hug lauvhyttone
me bygde
då me var små:
krjupa inn i dei, sitja
og lyda etter regnet,
vita seg einsam i villmarki,
kjenna dropane på nasen
og i håret—
Eller snøhusi i joli,
krjupa inn og
stengja etter seg med ein sekk,
kveikja ljos, vera der
i kalde kveldar.

Leaf Huts And Snow Houses

These poems don't amount
to much, just
some words thrown together
at random.
And still
to me
there's something good
in making them, it's
as if I have in them for a little
while a house.
I think of playhouses
made of branches we built
when we were children:
to crawl into them, sit
listening to the rain,
in a wild place alone,
feel the drops of rain on your nose
and in your hair –
or snowhouses at Christmas,
crawl in and close it after
with a sack,
light a candle, be there
through the long chill evenings.

∫ 47 ∫

Tid Å Hausta Inn

Desse milde soldagane i september.
Tid å hausta inn. Enno er det tuvor
med tytebær i skogen, njupone rodnar
langs steingardane, netene losnar,
og svarte klasar av bjønnebær skin i kjerri,
trasti leitar etter dei siste vinbæri,
og kvefsen syg ut dei søte plomone.
I kveldingi set eg stigen burt og hengjer
laupen frå meg i skuret. Skrinne bredar
har alt ei tunn breidsle av nysnø.
Etter eg er lagd, høyrer eg dunk frå brislingfiskarane,
dei gjeng ut. All natti veit eg dei glid
med sterke ljoskastarar og leitar yver fjorden.

Harvest Time

These calm days of September with their sun.
It's time to harvest. There are still clumps
of cranberries in the woods, reddening rosehips
by the stone walls, hazel nuts coming loose,
and clusters of black berries shine in the bushes;
thrushes look around for the last currants
and wasps fasten on to the sweetening plums.
I set the ladder aside at dusk, and hang
my basket up in the shed. The glaciers
all have a thin sprinkling of new snow. In bed
I hear the brisling fishermen start their motors
and go out. They'll pass the whole night
gliding over the fjord behind their powerful searchlights.

Note on the Norwegian Text

Olav H. Hauge writes in "country-Norwegian" that has been spoken for centuries on the farms. Most well-known Norwegian writers, Ibsen, Olaf Bull, and Rolf Jacobsen among them, have used "city-Norwegian" or Dano-Norwegian, influenced by the long Danish occupation. Some Norwegians feel the country Norwegian to be less harsh in its pronunciation, more vegetative, more calm, more alive.

The poems appear here in rough chronological order. The following poems are from *På Ornetuva* (1961): "Don't Come To Me With The Entire Truth," "Smoke," "I Open The Curtain," "Smoke," and "Kuppern On Skates In Squaw Valley." The following poems are from *Dropar i Austavind* (1966): "Winter Morning," "Berthold Brecht," "Today I Understood," "Across The Swamp," "There Is Nothing So Scary," "I Stand Here," "Yunnerstand," "Up On Top," "One Word," and "You Are The Wind." The following poems are from *Spør Vinden* (1971): "Midwinter. Snow," "December Moon 1969," "You Ride On Still," "I Look At The Stamp," "Looking At An Old Mirror," "Leaf Huts And Snow Houses," and "Harvest Time."

Olav H. Hauge was born in Ulvik, a village in the Hardanger fjord area of Norway, in 1908. He is a noted translator of the French symbolist poets and English and American writers into Norwegian. His books of poetry include *På Ornetuva* (1961), *Dropar i Austavind* (1966), *Spør Vinden* (1971), *Dikt i Samling* (1972, revised in 1980 and 1985), and a children's book of poetry, *ABC* (1986). Hauge still resides in Ulvik, and has lived his entire life on the proceeds from a single acre of apples. He was married for the first time five years ago to Bodil Cappelen, an artist.

Robert Bly was born in Minnesota in 1926. His first book, *Silence in the Snowy Fields*, was published in 1962; four years lated he founded, with David Ray, American Writers Against the Vietnam War. His second book, *The Light Around the Body*, was published in 1967 and received The National Book Award that year. Since then, he has published *The Morning Glory, Sleepers Joining Hands, This Tree Will Be Here For A Thousand Years, This Body Is Made of Camphor and Gopherwood, The Man in the Black Coat Turns*, and in 1986, *Selected Poems*. He has also published ten books of translations. His newest book is *The Winged Life: Selected Poetry and Prose of Thoreau* published by Sierra Club Books.

Kaare Espolin Johnson was born in Surnadal, Norway in 1907. He has been represented in numerous international exhibits, and has had one-man shows in Norway, Yugoslavia, and the United States. One of the best-known of Norwegian artists, he is noted for his scenes depicting the nature and folk culture of northern Norway. Johnson works mostly in black and white; even his oil paintings are studies in the relationships of dark and light. He has illustrated a notable series of books for the Gyldendal Norsk Forlag; it is from one of these, *Den Siste Viking*, that the graphics in this book are drawn.

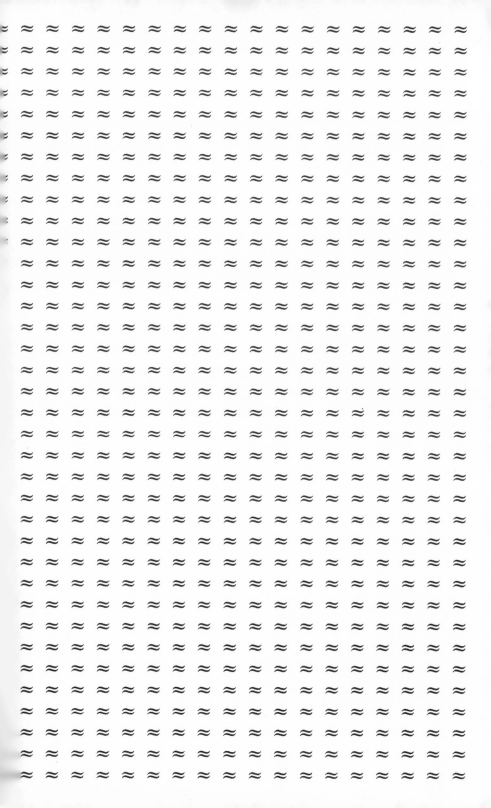

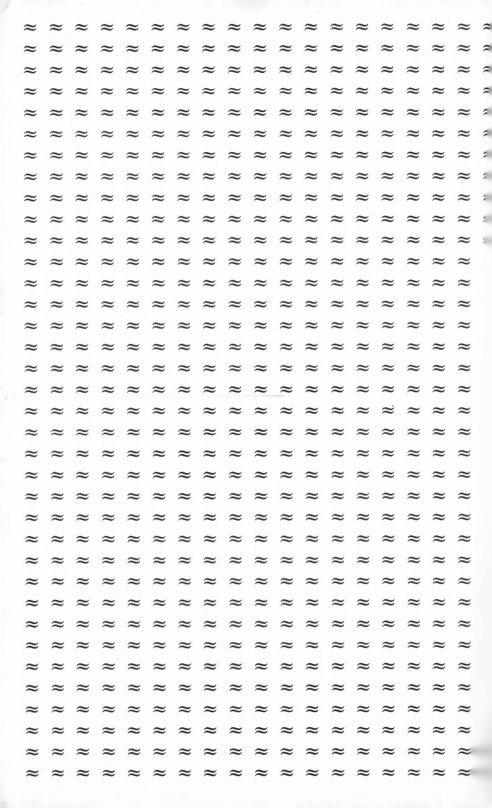